SOUNDS OF LANGUAGE
readers

SOUNDS OF LANGUAGE
SOUNDS OF LANGUAGE
SOUNDS OF LANGUAGE
SOUNDS OF LANGUAGE
LANGUAGE
LANGUAGE

SOUNDS

Holt, Rinehart and Winston, Inc.

New York   Toronto   London   Sydney

OF NUMBERS

BY BILL MARTIN JR.
IN COLLABOR
ATION WITH **PEGGY BROGAN**

6789   071   98765432

The Author and Holt, Rinehart and Winston, Inc. thank the following authors and publishers, whose help and permissions to reprint materials have made this book possible. All reasonable effort has been made to locate the source of every selection. If any errors in acknowledgments have occurred, they are inadvertent and will be corrected in subsequent editions as they are realized.

The following selections are adapted from Little Owl Books, copyright © 1963 by Holt, Rinehart and Winston, Inc., except as noted.

"Baby Chick," picture from *Poetry for Young Scientists*, a Young Owl Book, compiled by Leland B. Jacobs and Sally Nohelty, copyright © 1964 by Holt, Rinehart and Winston, Inc.

"Fog," "One Misty Moisty Morning," and "The North Wind Doth Blow," pictures from *Poems for Weather Watching*, compiled by Laurie Israel.

"Good Night, Mr. Beetle," text from *Good Night, Mr. Beetle*, by Leland B. Jacobs.

"One, Two, Three, Four," from *One, Two, Three, Four*, by Kate Considine and Ruby Schuler.

"Ten Pennies for Candy," from *Ten Pennies for Candy*, by Henry Ritchet Wing.

"Three Little Dachshunds," from *Three Little Dachshunds*, copyright 1954, © 1963 by Margaret G. Otto and Barbara Cooney.

"Twinkle, Twinkle, Little Star," picture from *The Sun Is a Star*, by Sune Engelbrektson.

"What Is Big?" text from *What Is Big?*, by Henry Ritchet Wing.

"What Is Pink?" from *What Is Pink?* by Christina G. Rossetti.

Other sources:

Abelard-Schuman, Ltd., for "Baby Chick," from *Runny Days, Sunny Days*, by Aileen Fisher, copyright © 1958 by Abelard-Schuman, Ltd. All rights reserved. Reprinted by permission.

Beckley-Cardey Company, for "Who Is Tapping at My Window?" by A. G. Deming. Reprinted by permission.

Edith Newlin Chase, for an excerpt from her poem, "The Fog Horn."

Aileen Fisher, for "Puppy," from *Up the Windy Hill*, by Aileen Fisher, copyright 1953 by Aileen Fisher. Published by Abelard-Schuman, 1953. Reprinted by permission.

Little, Brown and Company, for "Notice," from *Far and Few*, by David McCord, copyright 1952 by David McCord. Reprinted by permission of the author and publisher.

The Macmillan Company, for "The Little Turtle," from *Collected Poems*, by Vachel Lindsay, copyright 1920 by The Macmillan Company, renewed 1948 by Elizabeth C. Lindsay.

Acknowledgment is also made to Betty Jean Martin for permission to use the character, Noodles the Ghost, in this edition of Sounds of Numbers.

And no acknowledgment list would be complete without special thanks and appreciation to Phyllis Stevens and Lydia Vita for their skilled preparation of this book for delivery to the printer.

ACKNOWLEDGMENTS

CONTENTS

This book is dedicated affectionately
to **NOODLES**
who keeps the heartfires glowing

SOUNDS OF NUMBERS

One,
Two,
Buckle My Shoe,

Three, four,
Shut the door,

Five, six,
Pick up sticks,

Nine, ten,
A big fat hen.

Seven, eight,
Lay them straight,

an old rhyme,
illustrated by Peter Lippman

Little Ducky Duddle

went wading in a puddle,

went wading in a puddle quite small;

Said he, "It doesn't matter

how much I splash and splatter—

I'm only a ducky after all."

a traditional rhyme, adapted by Bill Martin Jr.
pictures by Leon Winik.

Little froggie woggie
went swimming in a boggie,
went swimming in a boggie quite small;
Said he, "It doesn't matter
how much I splash and splatter—
I'm only a froggie after all."

Little mousey wousey
   went running through the housie
   went running through the housie
      quite small;
Said he, "It doesn't matter
   how much I clang and clatter—
   the kitty is my best friend
      after all."

17

Mary Middling had a pig

not very little, not very big,
not very pink, not very green,
not very dirty, not very clean,

an old rhyme

by Ray Barber

pictures by Sal Murdocca hand lettered

not very good, not very naughty,
not very humble, not very haughty,
not very thin, not very fat;
NOW what would you give for a pig like that?

What Is Big?
PART I
by Henry Ritchet Wing,
pictures by Margaret Soucheck Cranstoun

My name is Tommy.
I am not very big.

I am not as big as a goat.
A goat is bigger than I am.

I am not as big as a horse.
A horse is bigger than I am.

I am not as big as an elephant.
An elephant is bigger than I am.

I am not as big as a whale.
A whale is bigger than I am.

I am not as big as a dinosaur.
A dinosaur **is the biggest**

thing I know.

Here's a Picture for Storytelling

by George Buckett

This

This land
is my

a song by Woody Guthrie,

design by Tom Huffman

is
your
land

From CALIFORNIA

From the redwood forest to the gulf

to New York ISLAND

strea-m WATERS

This land was made for

photograph *Golden Gate Bridge* by David Muench
photograph *New York Skyline* by Louis Goldman
painting *Seascape* by Henninger
drawings of children by Kelly Oechsli

What Is Pink?

a poem by Christina G. Rossetti, with pictures by Margaret Cranstoun

A rose is pink
By the fountain's brink.

What is red?

A poppy's red
In its barley bed.

What is white?

A swan is white
Sailing in the light.

What is blue?

The sky is blue
Where the clouds float thro'.

What is yellow?

Pears are yellow,
Rich and ripe and mellow.

What is green?

The grass is green,
With small flowers between.

What is violet?

Clouds are violet
In the summer twilight.

What is orange?

Why, an orange,

Just an orange!

The Purple Cow

by Gelett Burgess

I never saw a Purple Cow,
 I never hope to see one;
But I can tell you, anyhow,
 I'd rather see than be one.

picture by
Robert Jon Antler

GHOST

The Little Man
Who Wasn't There

by Hughes Mearns

As I was going up the stair
    I met a man who wasn't there!
He wasn't there again today!
    I wish, I wish he'd stay away!

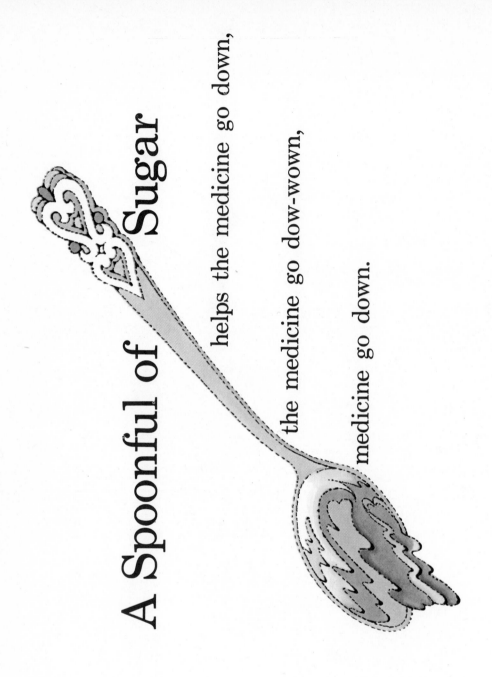

A Spoonful of Sugar

helps the medicine go down,

the medicine go dow-wown,

medicine go down.

a song from the motion picture "Mary Poppins"

Just a spoonful of sugar

helps the medicine go down

in the most delightful way.

by Richard M. Sherman and Robert B. Sherman, with pictures by Cornelio Martinez

Who Is Tapping at My Window?

a poem by A. G. Deming, picture by Margaret Cranstoun

"It's not I," said the cat.
"It's not I," said the rat.

"It's not I," said the wren.
"It's not I," said the hen.

"It's not I," said the fox.
"It's not I," said the ox.

"It's not I," said the loon.
"It's not I," said the coon.

"It's not I," said the cony.
"It's not I," said the pony.

"It's not I," said the dog.
"It's not I," said the frog.

"It's not I," said the hare.
"It's not I," said the bear.

"It is I," said the rain,
"tapping at your windowpane."

One, Two, Three, Four

by Kate Considine and Ruby Schuler,
pictures by Robert J. Lee

In the first month of the year,
I found 1 brown pony,
and he followed me home.

In the second month of the year,
I found 2 white kittens,
and they followed me home.

In the third month of the year,
I found 3 blue jays,
and they followed me home.

In the fourth month of the year,
I found 4 speckled chickens,
and they followed me home.

In the fifth month of the year,
I found 5 brown squirrels,
and they followed me home.

In the sixth month of the year,
I found 6 spotted puppies,
and they followed me home.

In the seventh month of the year,
I found 7 green frogs,
and they followed me home.

In the eighth month of the year,
I found 8 white rabbits,
and they followed me home.

In the ninth month of the year,
I found 9 white ducks,
and they followed me home.

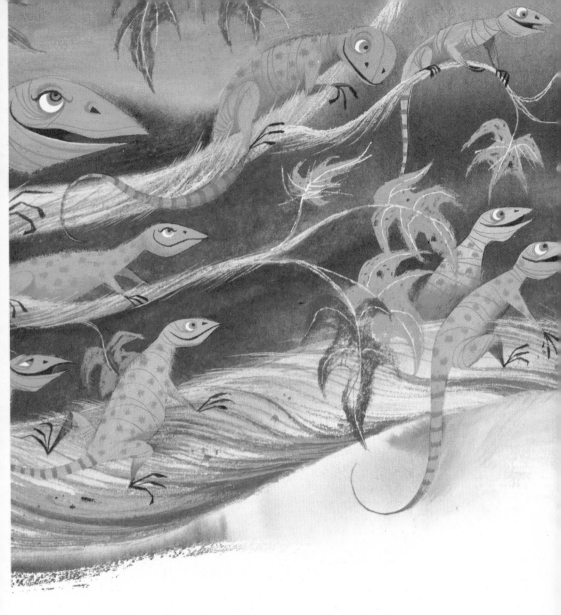

In the tenth month of the year,
I found 10 pink lizards,
and they followed me home.

In the eleventh month of the year,
I found 11 fat turkeys
and they followed me home.

In the twelfth month of the year,
I found 12 striped chipmunks,
and they followed me home.

Then Father and Mother said,
"Please! No more pets!"

BUT YOU CAN KEEP ME

One Misty, Moisty Morning

When cloudy was the weather,
I chanced to meet an old man
Clothed all in leather.
He began to compliment
And I began to grin:
"How do you do?"
And "How do you do?"
And "How do you do?" again.

a Mother Goose rhyme,
picture by Gilbert Riswold

Fog

Foggy, foggy over the water,
Foggy, foggy over the bay,
And through the fog
The boats go slowly
While the fog horn tells them the way.

by Edith Newlin Chase

What Is Big?
PART II
by Henry Ritchet Wing,
pictures by Margaret Cranstoun

My name is Tommy.

I am not very big.

But...

I am bigger
than a dog.

A dog is bigger than a cat.
I am bigger than a cat.

A cat is bigger than a mouse.
I am bigger than a mouse.

A mouse is bigger
than a grasshopper.
I am bigger than a grasshopper.

A grasshopper

is bigger

than a ladybug.

A ladybug
is
the
smallest
thing
I
know.

GOOD NIGHT, Mr. Beetle,

GOOD NIGHT, Miss Kitten, GOOD NIGHT, Mr. Pup, I'll see you in the morning when the sun comes up............ Mrs. Ladybug, the moon's in the sky, GOOD NIGHT, Mr. Fly, GOOD NIGHT,

pictures by Symeon Shimin

GOOD MORNING,
Mr. Beetle,
GOOD MORNING,
Mr. Fly,
GOOD MORNING,
Mrs. Ladybug, the sun's

ing. -wo-ı crow- the rooster crow-

GOOD MORNING, Mr. Pup, listen to the rooster crow-ing.

GOOD MORNING, Miss Kitten,

in the sky. GOOD MORNING,

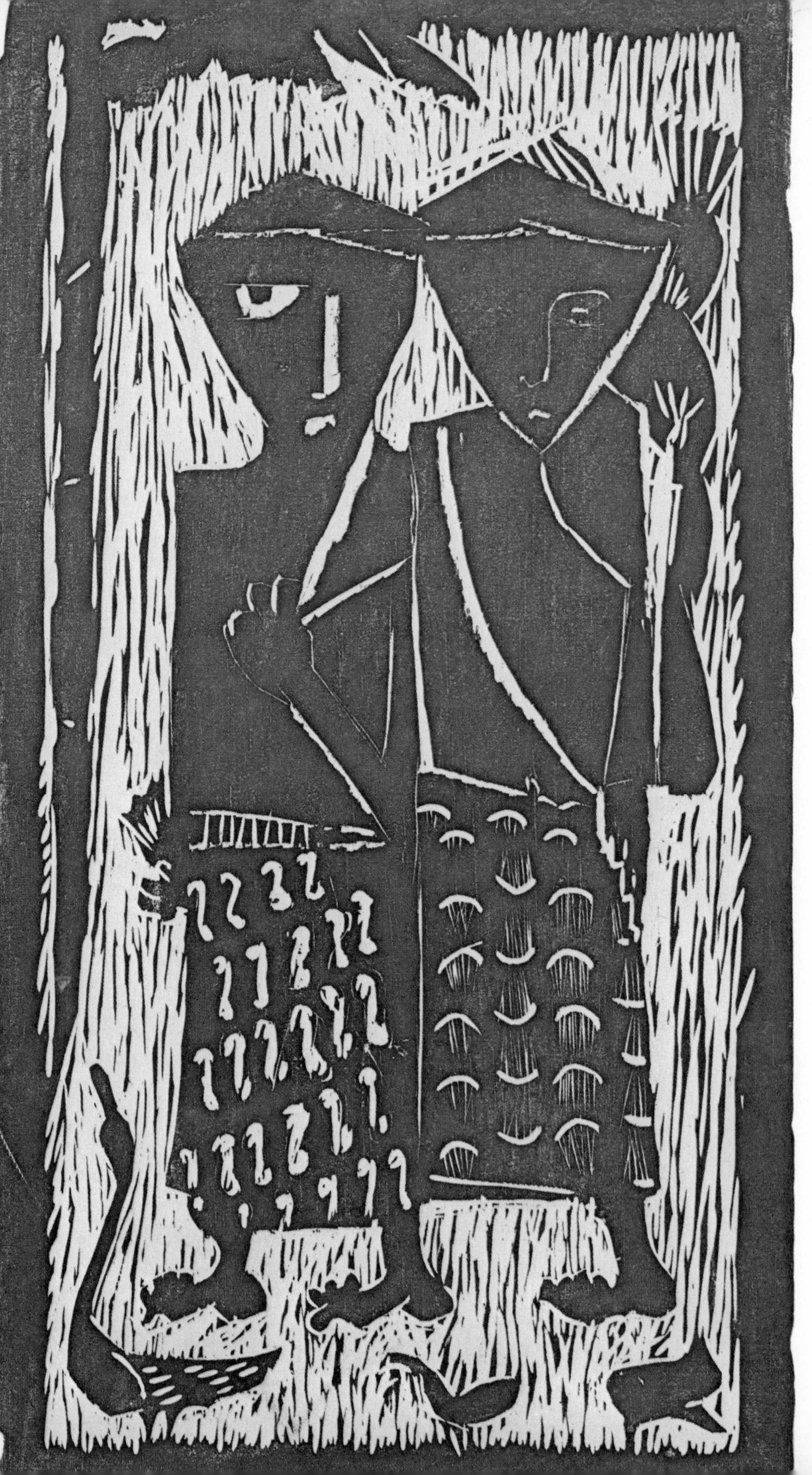

The Rice Pickers, woodcut by Sudjane Kerton

Sing a Song of Sixpence

A pocket full of rye,
Four and twenty blackbirds,
Baked in a pie.
When the pie was opened,
The birds began to sing.
Wasn't that a dainty dish,
To set before the King?

The King was in his counting house,
Counting out his money;
The Queen was in the parlor,
Eating bread and honey;
The maid was in the garden,
Hanging out the clothes.
Along came a blackbird,
And snipped off her nose.

a Mother Goose rhyme

Ten Pennies for Candy

by Henry Ritchet Wing,
pictures by Kelly Oechsli

Sandy said,

"Mother, I'm going to the store now."

"All right, Sandy," said Mother.

"Your money is on the table."

"Oh boy!" said Sandy.

"Ten pennies for candy."

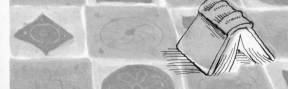

Sandy ran down the street.

"Come on, Andy!" said Sandy.

"I have 10 pennies for candy."

Sandy and Andy
ran down the street.

"Come on, Larry!" said Sandy.
"I have ten pennies for candy."

Sandy and Andy
and Larry
ran down the street.

"Come on, Mary!" said Sandy.
"I have ten pennies for candy."

Sandy and Andy
and Larry and Mary
ran down the street.

"Come on, Harry!" said Sandy.

"I have ten pennies for candy."

Sandy and Andy
and Larry and Mary and Harry
ran down the street.

"Come on, Sam!" said Sandy.
"I have ten pennies for candy."

Sandy and Andy
and Larry and Mary and Harry
and Sam
ran down the street.

"Come on, Sarah!" said Sandy.

"I have ten pennies for candy."

Sandy and Andy
and Larry and Mary and Harry
and Sam and Sarah
ran down the street.

"Come on, Freddy!" said Sandy.

"I have ten pennies for candy."

Sandy and Andy
and Larry and Mary and Harry
and Sam and Sarah
and Freddy
ran down the street.

"Come on, Eddie!" said Sandy.

"I have ten pennies for candy."

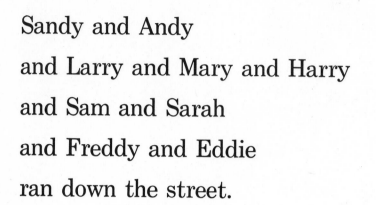

Sandy and Andy
and Larry and Mary and Harry
and Sam and Sarah
and Freddy and Eddie
ran down the street.

At last they came to the candy store.

"Hello, Mr. Moore," said Sandy.

"I have ten pennies for candy.

I want one piece of candy

for each penny."

"Ten pennies," said Mr. Moore.

He counted the pennies.

"Will ten pieces of candy

be enough?"

Sandy counted his friends.

"Yes," said Sandy.

"Ten pieces of candy will be enough.

   A piece of candy for each of my friends,

one for me,

and one......

Notice

by David McCord

I have a dog,
I had a cat.
I've got a frog
Inside my hat.

Puppy

by Aileen Fisher

My puppy likes
a hard old bone
as if it were
an ice-cream cone.

picture by Margaret Soucheck Cranstoun

Skip, Skip,
Skip to my Lou!
Skip, skip,
Skip to my Lou!
Skip, skip,
Skip to my Lou!
Skip to my Lou, my darling!

Flies in the buttermilk,
Shoo! shoo! shoo!
Flies in the buttermilk,
Shoo! shoo! shoo!
Flies in the buttermilk,
Shoo! shoo! shoo!
Skip to my Lou, my darling!

an American folk song,
painting by Stephania

a poem by Vachel Lindsay

pictures by Greg and Tim Hildebrandt

THERE WAS A LITTLE TURTLE.
HE LIVED IN A BOX.
HE SWAM IN A PUDDLE.
HE CLIMBED ON THE ROCKS.

HE SNAPPED AT A MOSQUITO.
HE SNAPPED AT A FLEA.
HE SNAPPED AT A MINNOW
AND HE SNAPPED AT ME.

HE CAUGHT
THE MOSQUITO.
HE CAUGHT THE FLEA.
HE CAUGHT THE MINNOW.

BUT HE DIDN'T CATCH ME.

135

The North Wind Doth Blow
And we shall have snow,
And what shall poor Robin do then?
Poor thing!

a Mother Goose rhyme,
picture by Gilbert Riswold

He'll sit in the barn
And keep himself warm,
And hide his head under his wing.
Poor thing!

Here's a Picture for Storytelling

by George Buckett

by Margaret G. Otto,
pictures by Barbara Cooney

Three Little Dachshunds. One, two, three.

Three little dachshunds.
See how they run!

Three little dachshunds.
One, two, three.
Three little dachshunds
in one little bed.

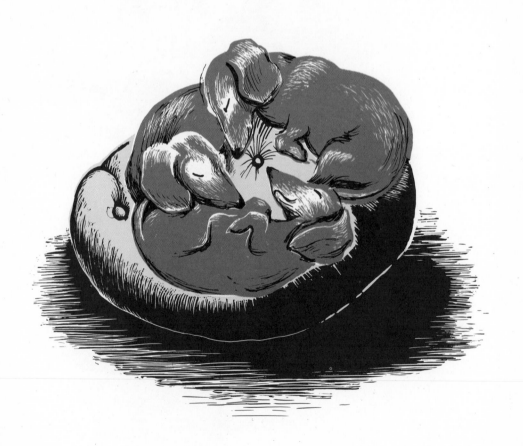

Three little dachshunds
go to the store.
They go to the store
with Old Miss Marvelous.

Three little dachshunds
walk home from the store.
They walk home
with Old Miss Marvelous.

Two little children
see three little dachshunds.
"Hello, little dachshunds.
We are your friends."

Three little dachshunds
run to the woods.
One, two, three,
they run to the woods.

Three little dachshunds
see a gray squirrel.
"Bow-wow-wow!"
say three little dachshunds.

Three little dachshunds
see a red bird.
"Bow-wow-wow!"
say three little dachshunds.

"Bow-wow-wow,"
   says the first little dachshund.
"We are lost."

"Bow-wow-wow,"
   says the second little dachshund.
"Yes, we are lost."

"Bow-wow-wow,"
   says the third little dachshund.
"Lost we are."

Three little dachshunds
bark and bark.
Three little dachshunds
want to go home.

Two little children
hear three little dachshunds.
"Listen!" say the children.
"The dachshunds are lost!
Here, little dachshunds!
Come to your friends!
Come, little dachshunds!
Come home! Come home!"

Three little dachshunds
run to their friends.
They jump and bark
and run to their friends.

Two little children
take the dogs home.
They take the dogs home
to Old Miss Marvelous.

Old Miss Marvelous is very happy.
"Thank you, children,
  for finding my dogs.
And you bad little dachshunds!
Where have you been?"

"Here is a surprise,"
says Old Miss Marvelous.
"A thank-you surprise
for two good friends."

"Bow-wow-wow!"
say three little dachshunds.
"We like surprises,
and we like home!"

Baby Chick

by Aileen Fisher,
picture by Ed Young

Peck
    peck
        peck
on the warm brown egg.
OUT comes a neck.
OUT comes a leg.

How
    does
        a chick,
who's not been about,
discover the trick
of how to get out?

Twinkle, Twinkle Little Star

How I wonder what you are.

Up above the world so high

Like a diamond in the sky.

Twinkle, twinkle little star

How I wonder what you are.

a rhyme by Jane Taylor,
picture by Eric Carle